This annual belongs to

....

....

EGMONT
We bring stories to life

First published in Great Britain 2013
by Egmont UK Limited,
The Yellow Building, 1 Nicholas Road, London W11 4AN

Text by Gemma Barder. • Design by Pritty Ramjee.
© 2013 Prism Art & Design Limited, a HIT Entertainment company. Based on an
original idea by D. Gingell, D. Jones and original characters created by R. J. M. Lee.
All rights reserved.

ISBN 978 1 4052 6759 5
54718/2
Printed in Italy

HiT entertainment

Stay safe online. Any website addresses listed in this book are correct at the time of going to print. However, Egmont is not
responsible for content hosted by third parties. Please be aware that online content can be subject to change and websites
can contain content that is unsuitable for children. We advise that all children are supervised when using the internet.

Adult supervision is recommended when glue, paint, scissors and other sharp points are in use.

CONTENTS

A chance to win £150 of book tokens!

NATIONAL BOOK tokens

See page 67 for details.

MEET THE RESCUE TEAM

Elvis

Elvis is always on hand to help Sam. He loves singing and playing his guitar, too!

Fireman Sam

Sam is the hero of Pontypandy. He always knows what to do in an emergency!

Station Officer Steele

Station Officer Steele is in charge of Pontypandy Fire Station. He likes things to be in order.

Penny

Penny is a brave firefighter. She drives Jupiter and Neptune and is great with emergencies at sea, too!

Tom Thomas

Tom is a brave pilot who runs the Mountain Rescue Centre. He's always ready for adventure!

Welcome to Pontypandy

Dilys and Norman

Dilys looks after the local shop with her son Norman. Norman always seems to be in trouble, but his mum loves him anyway!

The Jones family

Sarah and James are Fireman Sam's niece and nephew! Their dad Charlie is a fisherman and their mum Bronwyn runs the Wholefish Café.

Trevor Evans

Trevor drives the Pontypandy bus.

Moose Roberts

Moose runs the Mountain Adventure Centre and loves camping!

The Flood family

Mike Flood is the local handyman, but he's a bit clumsy! Luckily his wife Helen is a nurse. Their daughter Mandy is Norman's best friend.

Gareth Griffiths

Gareth is Sarah and James' grandad. He lives at the Mountain Railway Station and drives the train.

Mrs Chen and Lily

Mrs Chen is the Pontypandy schoolteacher and the only person Norman is scared of! Her little daughter Lily is lots of fun, but quite cheeky too!

11

MANDY → AT SEA

Charlie is teaching Mandy how to sail a boat. She wants to sail a yacht around the world!

Well done, Mandy. I reckon you're ready for a solo sail!

At the Fire Station, Fireman Sam and Penny are teaching Elvis to fix the engines.

Fixing things sounds very complicated!

"Don't worry," says Sam. "Penny will guide you through it."

"Let's start with something simple," says Penny. "Can you change the batteries in the radio?"

Elvis nods, but he drops the batteries on the floor. Station Officer Steele trips over them!

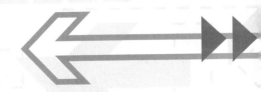

Maybe you should take Elvis to the Quay to work on Neptune!

At the Quay, everyone is waving Mandy off. She's going on her first solo sailing trip. They all cheer as she sails to the Lighthouse.

"Remember everything Charlie has taught you!" says Mandy's mum, Helen.

Meanwhile, Penny shows Elvis how to use a drill.

"It's right to tighten and left to loosen," she says. Elvis nods, but as he goes to use the drill, three bolts fall off Neptune.

"Oh dear!" says Elvis. Things are not going well.

Out at sea, Mandy is in trouble. The mast of her boat has snapped and she is floating out to sea! Everyone on the Quay is worried.

"We'd better call Fireman Sam!" said Charlie.

Fireman Sam rings Penny down by the sea. Penny jumps into Neptune as soon as she has taken the call.

But Elvis is worried about Neptune's missing bolts!

Penny, I'm sure those bolts are important.

Not now, Elvis. We have to get Mandy!

Mandy has spotted a piece of driftwood floating in the water.

"Great!" she says. "I can use this to make a mast and get my boat sailing again."

She sets to work right away.

Penny and Elvis hear a loud splash. The engine has fallen off the boat!

"I'm sorry," says Elvis. "I tried to tell you."

"It's my fault too," says Penny. "I should have listened to you."

At the Quay, Sam has found the missing bolts.

"These look important," he says. "I'd better call Tom – we're going to need Wallaby One!"

Tom and Sam jump into Wallaby One and head out to sea.

"Mandy Flood is in trouble, and I think Penny and Elvis might need help too!" says Sam.

On Neptune, Penny has used her diving skills to pick up the engine from the sea bed. Soon they hear Wallaby One. Sam lowers himself onto Neptune.

"I thought you might need these!" says Sam, holding out the bolts.

"Leave this to me!" says Elvis. He takes the bolts and confidently fixes the engine back onto the boat.

Well done, Elvis!

Soon, they hear a boat approaching. It's Mandy Flood!

"You've fixed your boat," says Penny.

"You can lead us to the Quay, Captain Mandy!" says Sam.

Mandy proudly leads the boats back. And when they arrive, everyone cheers!

THE END

SEA RESCUE

Charlie has fallen off his boat into the sea! Help Penny to rescue him, avoiding the buoys along the way.

START

Which rescue vehicle should Penny use to help Charlie?

Jupiter

Neptune

Rescue Jeep

Answers on page 66.

16

Penny and Sam

Colour in this picture of Penny and Sam getting ready for a rescue at sea!

17

ARE YOU AN EMERGENCY HERO?

Do you know how to stay safe? Add a tick (✓) by the things you should do and a cross (x) by the ones you shouldn't do!

1 Should you watch food as it cooks?

2 Should you test your smoke alarm?

3 Should you burn candles near curtains?

IF THERE IS A FIRE ...

4 Should you get out of the house?

5 Should you stop to get your valuables?

6 Should you phone 999?

Answers on page 66.

DID YOU KNOW...?

If food gets too hot, it can catch fire. Adults should turn the cooker down or off if they leave the kitchen.

Smoke alarms detect smoke before you can. Test them regularly to check if the batteries need to be replaced.

Candles can burn curtains! Adults must blow them out if they leave the room.

IF THERE IS A FIRE ...

Don't stop to get your valuables, they can be replaced.

Leave the house immediately so you are safe.

Call 999 and ask for the Fire Service. Give them your address so they can help as quickly as possible.

Lost Property

Draw a line to match each person to their property.

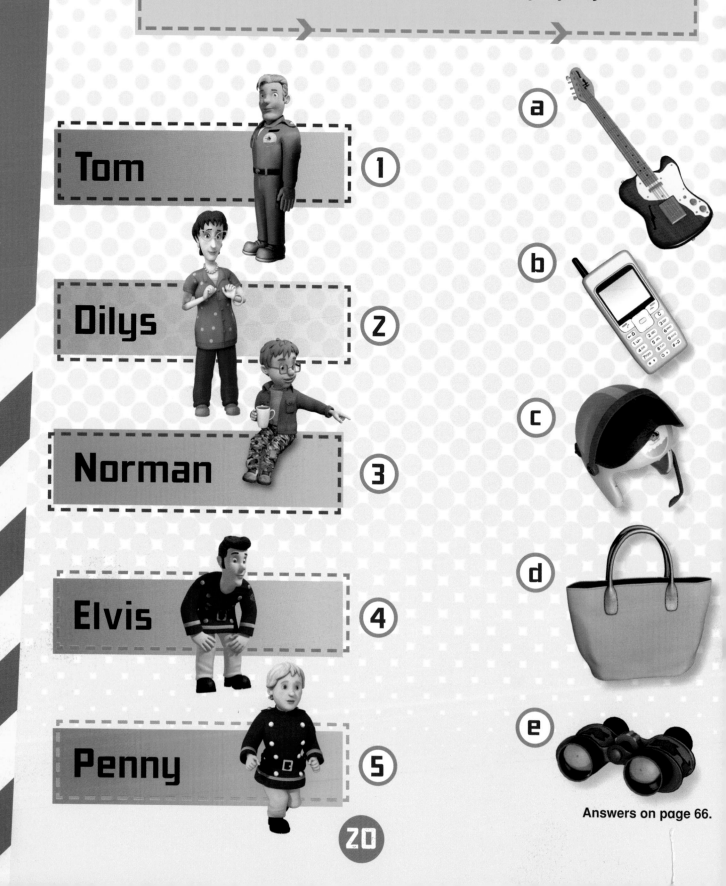

Tom   1

Dilys   2

Norman   3

Elvis   4

Penny   5

a

b

c

d

e

Answers on page 66.

Spot the Difference

Can you spot the five differences between these two pictures?

1

2

Answers on page 66.

Norman's Ghost

Officer Steele is visiting Dilys at the shop.

The shop is haunted!

"Don't be silly," says Officer Steele. "There's no such thing as ghosts!" Just then they hear a spooky noise …

Officer Steele finds the real cause of the noise.
It's Norman and Mandy!
Mandy giggles.

It wasn't me! It was Mandy!

I'm just getting ready for the Halloween party tonight!

Later that day, Mandy is helping to set up the party.

She sees the curtains blow and hears a spooky noise! But it's only Norman. "He he!" she giggles. "I know it's you, Norman!"

22

Norman is determined to scare someone so he hides in the house until the party starts.

Sarah and James have come to the party, too.

"I can't wait for the bonfire!" says Sarah.

As they open the door, Norman jumps out and gives a spooky cry! His friends all laugh.

"We know it's you, Norman!" says James.

Huh! I will spook you all! Just you wait!

Soon, Mandy's Mum Helen arrives.

It's time to light the Halloween pumpkin!

All the children cheer. The pumpkin looks very spooky with its eyes all lit up.

"Right, let's go outside and see the bonfire," says Helen.

But Norman has another idea.

"If I put this old sheet over the pumpkin it will look like a REAL ghost!" says Norman.

Outside the bonfire is blazing.

Mike Flood asks Norman to tell them a ghost story.

The Ghost of Pontypandy was wandering the empty streets!

Everyone giggles.

"What's so funny?" asks Norman. "The Ghost was dressed all in white. He came to this very house and stood by the window!"

Everyone giggles again.

Well, if you don't believe me – just look!

They turn to look at the window, but instead of a ghost, they see that the house is on fire!

"Call Fireman Sam!" cries Helen.

Everyone gets behind the garden wall to keep away from the fire.

Soon Fireman Sam arrives in Jupiter with Elvis and Officer Steele.

"Is it the bonfire?" he asks.

"It's the living room!" replies Mike.

"Better get our breathing apparatus on, men!" says Officer Steele.

Fireman Sam and the team soon put out the flames and make the living room safe again.

What happened?

We left the candle lit!

And left a cloth over it!

Sam shakes his head.

"You must NEVER leave a candle unattended and you must NEVER put a cloth over a naked flame."

"I'll help clear up the mess," says Norman. "It was my fault."

"It was mine, too!" says Helen.

"We'll all help," says Fireman Sam.

Everyone agrees that the scariest thing about Halloween wasn't the stories or costumes, it was the fire!

THE END

Shadow Spotting

Can you spot which shadow belongs to each character? Draw lines to match them up.

① ② ③ ④ ⑤

ⓐ ⓑ ⓒ ⓓ ⓔ

Answers on page 66.

Only 2 of these pictures of Norman playing superhero are exactly the same. Can you see which two they are?

a

c

b

d

e

Answer on page 66.

Double Trouble

Sarah and James can't wait to go skateboarding.
Colour them in before they go!

Bronwyn's Beach

Bronwyn is collecting shells. Can you help her to find 6 shells on the beach?

Answer on page 66.

Make Your Own Rescue Crew Badges

What to do

1. Colour in your badges.
2. When you've finished the book, cut out this page and glue it onto thin card.

3. Carefully cut out your badges.
4. Tape a safety pin to the back of each one.
5. Wear your badges with pride!

Ask an adult to help you with each step.

ELVIS
SINGS --→

Elvis loves to sing!
Can you find the missing
piece of the picture?

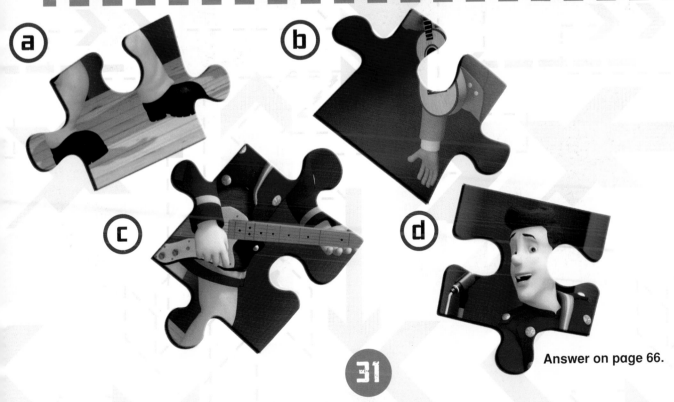

a

b

c

d

31

Answer on page 66.

Jupiter Fact File

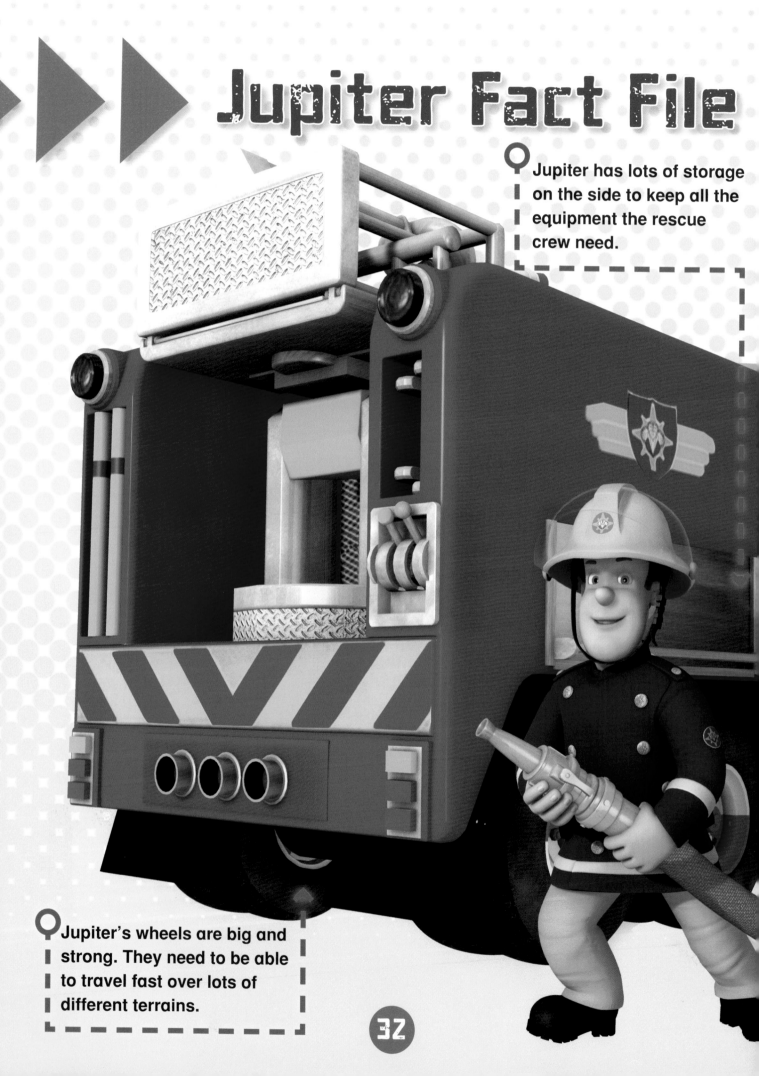

Jupiter has lots of storage on the side to keep all the equipment the rescue crew need.

Jupiter's wheels are big and strong. They need to be able to travel fast over lots of different terrains.

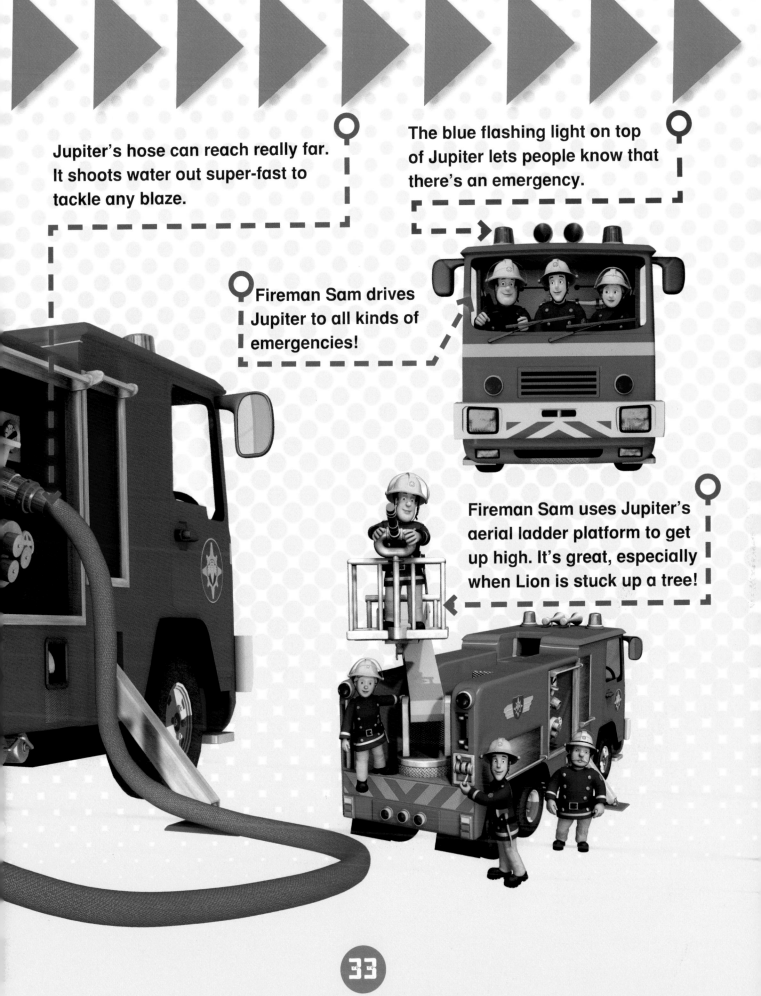

Jupiter's hose can reach really far. It shoots water out super-fast to tackle any blaze.

The blue flashing light on top of Jupiter lets people know that there's an emergency.

Fireman Sam drives Jupiter to all kinds of emergencies!

Fireman Sam uses Jupiter's aerial ladder platform to get up high. It's great, especially when Lion is stuck up a tree!

Alarm on the Beach

You can help read this story. Listen to the words and when you see a picture, say the name!

Sam

Penny

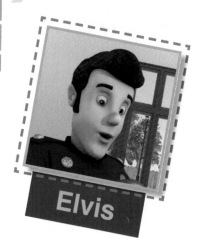

Sarah

James

Mandy

Elvis

One warm and sunny day, 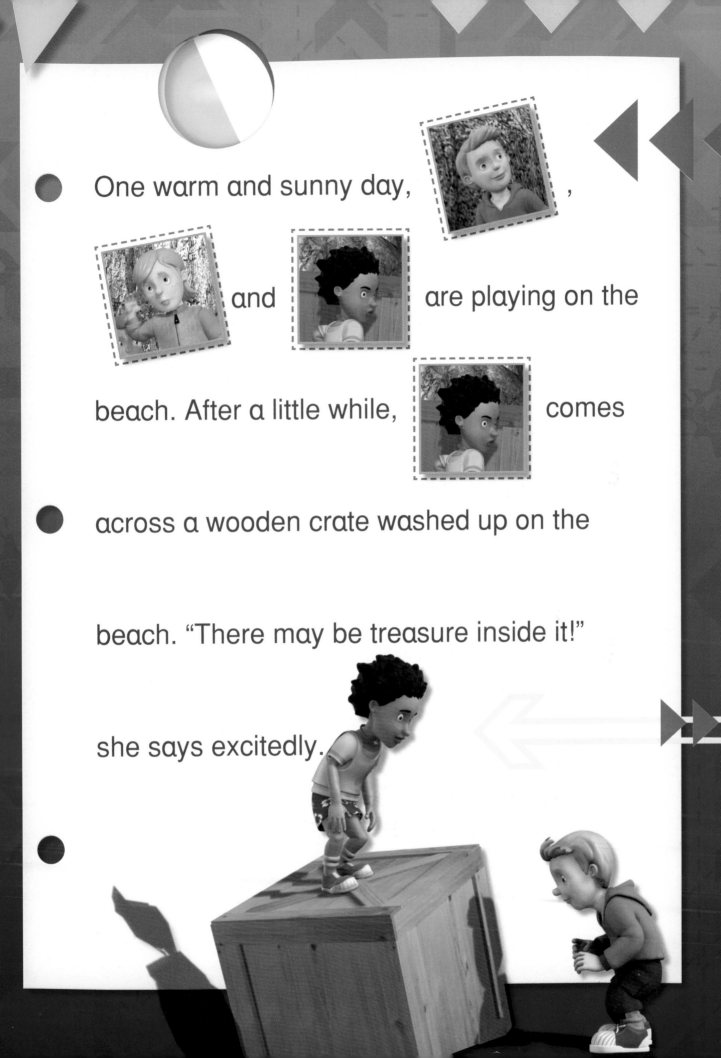 ,

and are playing on the

beach. After a little while, comes

across a wooden crate washed up on the

beach. "There may be treasure inside it!"

she says excitedly.

Meanwhile,  has gone to wake up

at his home. has slept in!

"You're late for work again," says

"Sorry," says . "I find it hard to wake

up in the morning." The two of them drive away

in Jupiter.

On the beach,  ,  and

 are trying to open the crate.

Suddenly, the heavy crate topples onto

 and traps his legs. He is stuck,

and there is a strange ticking noise coming

from the crate! runs to find a

phone and she calls the fire brigade.

 and  quickly arrive in

Jupiter.  is out at sea in Neptune.

She radios  to tell him where on

the beach the children are. The firefighters

soon find  and lift the crate off him.

"Hooray, I'm free! Thank you!" he says.

 is safe, but the crate is still ticking!

 carefully opens the crate and

peers inside. "The crate is full of alarm clocks,"

he laughs. He hands a clock to 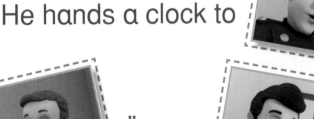 .

"Thanks,  ," says  .

"I need one of these to help wake me up in

the morning!"

SPOT THE DIFFERENCE

Fireman Sam and Officer Steele are pulling into the Fire Station.

1

True or False

Add a tick (✓) or a cross (x) to show whether these statements about Sam and the team are true or false.

1. Jupiter is green .... ☐
2. Neptune is a fire engine .... ☐
3. Penny is a firefighter .... ☐
4. Lion is a dog .... ☐
5. Tom flies Wallaby One .... ☐
6. Sam has grey hair .... ☐

Answers on page 66.

These pictures look the same but 5 things
are different in picture 2.

Circle the differences as you spot them.

2

Colour in Jupiter
when you've found
all 5 differences!

Answers on page 66.

Safety Patterns

Look at each line of pictures and say which safety item should come next. Draw the item in the space to finish the pattern.

1

2

3

Answers on page 66.

The Pontypandyness Monster

It's a lovely day in Pontypandy and Moose has a job for Mike.

"Can you fix the jetty on the lake" asks Moose.

"No problem!" say Mike.

The steam train puffs into the Mountain Activity Centre. There is only Sarah and James on the train. Not many people use the train anymore.

The train isn't as popular as it used to be.

What's this?

Moose shows the children a picture.

"This is the Pontypandyness Monster," says Moose. "Lots of people used to visit the lake to try to spot it!"

Suddenly Sarah has an idea. If she pretends she has seen the Pontypandyness Monster, people might want to visit the lake and her grandad will get lots more passengers.

"It's the Pontypandyness Monster!"

Gareth calls Bronwyn to tell her the monster news and soon everyone in Pontypandy has heard the exciting story!

Dilys is frightened, so she calls the Fire Station.

Station Officer Steele is surprised.

Elvis asks if he can go – he can't wait to see the monster!

The lake will be flooded with visitors. We'd better do a risk check.

45

At the lake, a whole train full of passengers has arrived.

Sarah shows everyone where she saw the monster, although she feels quite bad for lying about it.

A crowd of people rush down the jetty to get a better look.

Careful! The jetty isn't quite finished yet!

Just then, there is a loud crack and the end of the jetty breaks off!

It floats along the lake with lots of people still on it!

"James!" Moose shouts. "Call Fireman Sam!"

James runs back into the Activity Centre and calls the Fire Station for help.

In no time, Penny and Sam arrive at the lake.

Penny rows out to the stranded crowd and ties a rope to the jetty.

Back on land, Sam ties a rope to Mercury. They try to pull the jetty back to shore, but it's stuck!

Penny bravely dives in the water to see what the problem is. The jetty is caught in some reeds. She cuts it free.

Soon everyone is back on dry land.

"I didn't really see a monster," says Sarah, sadly. "I just wanted everyone to use my grandad's train."

"Don't worry," says Sam. "I'm sure we'll all be back for another visit on the train. Even if there isn't a Pontypandyness Monster."

Or is there?!

THE END

Learning Letters

Can you trace over the letters to write the names of two firemen friends?

Fireman

Sam

Elvis

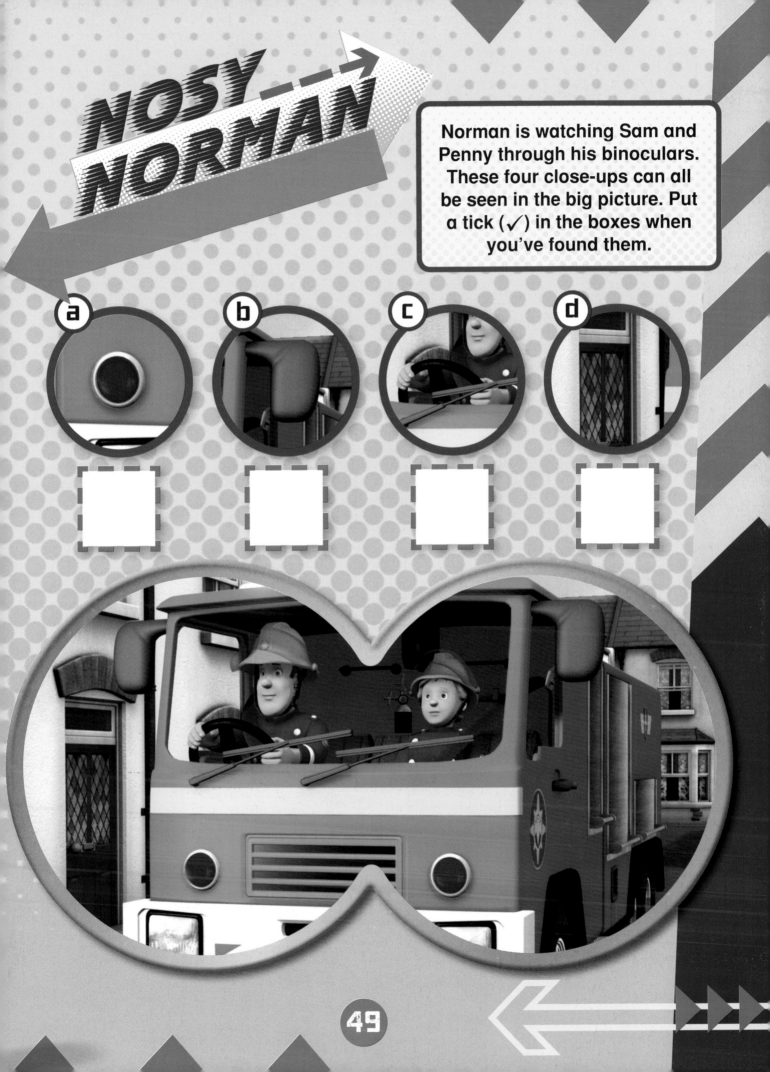

NOSY NORMAN

Norman is watching Sam and Penny through his binoculars. These four close-ups can all be seen in the big picture. Put a tick (✓) in the boxes when you've found them.

a b c d

Elvis Emergency!

Elvis is going to an emergency on the beach. Circle the things he needs in his kit.

Answers on page 66.

Firefighter Friends

Colour in this picture of Elvis and Sam!

RACE TO THE TOP

Tom and Penny have gone for a hike on Pontypandy Mountain and it's turned into a race! Who will reach the top first?

Find a short cut. Go forward 2 spaces.

How to play

You will need: a dice and a counter for each player.

- This is a game for 2 players. Decide who will be Penny and who will be Tom.
- Place the counters on the START square, then throw the dice and move around the board.
- Follow the instructions as you go, and if you land on a space with rocks on it, miss a turn.
- If you land on a space with a map, take a shortcut and zoom ahead by taking an extra turn.
- The first player to reach the FINISH is the winner!

START

FINISH

Stop to tie your laces. Go back 1 space.

Take a wrong turn. Miss 1 go.

Sprint to the finish. Go forward 1 space.

53

Sam and Lion

Use your brightest colours on this
picture of Sam and Lion!

SAM'S SUDOKU

Can you fit each item once in every row and column? Draw in the missing objects.

Helmet   **Fire Extinguisher**   **Life Jacket**   **Axe**

Answer on page 66.

Rescue Jeep

Answer the questions about Tom Thomas in his jeep.
Put a tick (✓) next to the correct answer each time.

a How many red circles are on the jeep?   2 ☐   4 ☐   6 ☐

b What colour are the 3 lights in a row on the bonnet?
Red ☐   White ☐   Blue ☐

c How many people are in the jeep?   1 ☐   2 ☐   4 ☐

d Count how many red stripes there are on the front.
4 ☐   5 ☐   6 ☐   7 ☐

Answers on page 66.

Skate Silhouette

Can you match the picture of Norman on his skateboard to the correct silhouette?

A

B

C

D

Sticky Situation

One warm sunny morning, Norman is walking around Pontypandy. He is listening to music on his MP3 player with his headphones on.

Norman is just about to step out in front of Trevor's bus. Luckily, Fireman Sam sees him and pulls him back.

SCREECH!!!

You can't hear the cars coming.

Fireman Sam tells Norman that crossing the road with headphones on is very dangerous.

"Sorry, Sam," says Norman. "I was listening to my new MP3 player. I got it for my birthday."

Later that day, Norman is building a model plane that Mandy gave him for his birthday.

Mandy notices that Norman has put his magnifying glass on a piece of card, and the sun is shining through it.

"Careful, Norman!" says Mandy. "The glass is in the sun."

But Norman is more concerned with his plane. He runs downstairs to find some strong glue.

Norman loses his temper and snaps at Mandy. Poor Mandy gets upset, and she leaves.

Back upstairs, the magnifying glass is in the sun again, and it's shining on the model's instructions. They start to smoke.

Oh!

Soon, a fire has started! Norman jumps and accidentally squirts some of the really strong glue on his hands.

He opens his bedroom door and calls for his mum.

MUM!

But downstairs in the shop, Dilys is listening to music on Norman's MP3 player. She doesn't hear Norman's calls.

Norman tries to run out of the room, but his hand gets stuck to the doorknob!

Norman thinks hard. He grabs one of his books, and he throws it at the model plane. The burning model is knocked out of the window ... into the path of Mike Flood who's driving his van below!

The plane lands right on Mike's bonnet! Mike stops the van and sees smoke coming from Norman's room. He quickly calls the Pontypandy Fire Station on his mobile phone.

Whoa! Where did that come from?

It's not long before Fireman Sam, Penny and Elvis arrive at the scene. Dilys still has the headphones on, and is shocked to see Fireman Sam and Penny burst through the shop, dragging a hose! Elvis tells her about the fire upstairs.

Fireman Sam and Penny find Norman upstairs. Seeing that Norman is glued to the door, Fireman Sam says that the whole door will quickly have to be taken off its hinges!

Fireman Sam soon puts the fire out, and everybody is safe. Penny takes Norman outside – still stuck to the door! She asks Dilys to find some nail varnish remover which will help unstick Norman's hand.

Thanks, Penny. If only I hadn't been wearing those headphones!

Later on, back inside the shop, Mike offers to help Norman make a new model plane.

"It's time to head back to the station now, Elvis," says Fireman Sam.

But Elvis can't hear him – he's too busy bopping away to a tune on Norman's MP3 player!

THE END

FOLLOW THE STORY

Now you've read Sticky Situation, can you remember what happened? Put the pictures in order by writing the letters in the boxes.

a

b

c

d

1
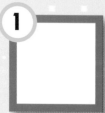

2

3

4

Answers on page 66.

NEE NAH!

Sam is driving by in Jupiter! Colour in the picture, using the colour code to help you.

ANSWERS

Page 16 SEA RESCUE

Penny should use Neptune to rescue Charlie.

Page 18 ARE YOU AN EMERGENCY HERO?

1: ✓, 2: ✓, 3: x, 4: ✓, 5: x, 6: ✓.

Page 20 LOST PROPERTY

1. Tom - **c**, 2. Dilys - **d**,
3. Norman - **e**, 4. Elvis - **a**,
5. Penny - **b**.

Page 21 SPOT THE DIFFERENCE

Page 26 SHADOW SPOTTING

1- **e**, 2 - **d**, 3 - **b**, 4 - **c**, 5 - **a**.

Page 27 MISCHIEF MAKER
Pictures **a** and **d** are the same.

Page 29 BRONWYN'S BEACH

Page 31 ELVIS SINGS
Piece **b** is missing from the picture.

Page 40 SPOT THE DIFFERENCE

TRUE OR FALSE

1: x, 2: x, 3: ✓, 4: x, 5: ✓, 6: x.

Page 42 SAFETY PATTERNS

Page 50 ELVIS EMERGENCY

Axe and Helmet.

Page 55 SAM'S SUDOKU

Page 56 RESCUE JEEP

a - **4**, b - white, c - **1**, d - **7**.

Page 57 SKATE SILHOUETTE

B is the correct silhouette.

Page 64 FOLLOW THE STORY

1 - **c**, 2 - **d**, 3 - **b**, 4 - **a**.

Reader Survey

We'd love to know what you think about your Fireman Sam Annual.

Ask a grown-up to help you fill in this form and post it to the address at the end by 28th February 2014, or you can fill in the survey online at: www.egmont.co.uk/firemansamsurvey2014

One lucky reader will win £150 of book tokens!
Five runners-up will win a £25 book token each.

1. Who bought this annual?

☐ Me
☐ Parent/guardian
☐ Grandparent
☐ Other (please specify)

....

2. Why did they buy it?

☐ Christmas present
☐ Birthday present
☐ I'm a collector
☐ Other (please specify)

....

3. What are your favourite parts of the annual?

Stories	☐ Really like	☐ Like	☐ Don't like
Puzzles	☐ Really like	☐ Like	☐ Don't like
Colouring	☐ Really like	☐ Like	☐ Don't like
Drawing	☐ Really like	☐ Like	☐ Don't like
Games	☐ Really like	☐ Like	☐ Don't like

4. Do you think the stories are too long, too short or about right?

☐ Too long
☐ Too short
☐ About right

5. Do you think the activities are too hard, too easy or about right?

☐ Too hard
☐ Too easy
☐ About right

6. Apart from Fireman Sam, who are your favourite characters?

1. ....
2. ....
3. ....

7. Which other annuals have you bought this year?

1. ....
2. ....
3. ....

8. What is your favourite ...

1. ... app? ....
2. ... website? ....
3. ... console game? ....
4. ... magazine? ....
5. ... book? ....

9. What are your favourite TV programmes?

1. ....
2. ....
3. ....

10. Would you like to get the Fireman Sam Annual again next year?

☐ Yes
☐ No
Why? ....
....

Thank you! (Please ask your parent/guardian to complete)

Child's name: .... Age: .... Boy/Girl

Parent/guardian name: ....

Parent/guardian signature: ....

Parent/guardian email address: ....

Daytime telephone number: ....

Good luck!

☐ Please send me the Egmont Monthly Catch-Up Newsletter.
Please cut out this form and post to:
Fireman Sam Annual Reader Survey,
Egmont UK Limited, The Yellow Building, 1 Nicholas Road, London, W11 4AN

DON'T MISS FIREMAN SAM MAGAZINE!
IT'S FULL OF FIREFIGHTING ACTION!

ON SALE EVERY 4 WEEKS!

Help me fight this fire!

FREE GIFT WITH EVERY ISSUE!

FIND IT IN ALL GOOD NEWSAGENTS AND SUPERMARKETS NOW!